OXFORD BOOKWORMS LIBRARY
Classics

The Prince and the Pauper

MARK TWAIN

Stage 2 (700 headwords)

Retold by Alex Raynham
Illustrated by Iva Sasheva

Series Editor: Rachel Bladon
Founder Editors: Jennifer Bassett
and Tricia Hedge

OXFORD
UNIVERSITY PRESS

Great Clarendon Street, Oxford, OX2 6DP, United Kingdom

Oxford University Press is a department of the University of Oxford.
It furthers the University's objective of excellence in research, scholarship,
and education by publishing worldwide. Oxford is a registered trade
mark of Oxford University Press in the UK and in certain other countries

ISBN: 978 0 19 423789 5

A complete recording of this Bookworms edition of
The Prince and the Pauper is available on audio CD. ISBN: 0 19 423787 1

Printed in China

Word count (main text): 9,304 words

For more information on the Oxford Bookworms Library,
visit www.oup.com/elt/gradedreaders

ACKNOWLEDGEMENTS

The publisher would like to thank the following for their permission to reproduce photographs:
Alamy p.55 (Henry VIII/GL Archive)

Illustrations by: Iva Sasheva/The Bright Agency

Picture research and illustration commissioning: Alison Wright

CONTENTS

PEOPLE IN THIS STORY

Tom Canty a pauper who lives in Offal Court
Edward Tudor a prince who lives in the Palace
  of Westminster

At Offal Court

John Canty Tom's father
Mrs Canty Tom's mother
Bet and Nan Tom's sisters
Old Andrew Tom's friend and teacher

At the Palace of Westminster

Lady Jane Grey Edward's cousin
King Henry the Eighth Edward's father
Lord Hertford an important lord
Princess Elizabeth Edward's sister

Other People in this Story

Duke of Norfolk King Henry the Eighth's enemy
Miles Hendon a soldier who helps Edward
Hugo a boy in a gang of thieves

CHAPTER I

Rags and Riches

Tom Canty was born one autumn day in London. It was 1537, and the Canty family were very poor. They did not want another child!

Edward Tudor was born on the same day, but he was the son of King Henry the Eighth, and his family wanted him very much. All England wanted him, too. At last, the country had a prince! High and low, rich and poor, the people of England ate, sang, and danced.

People talked only of the baby prince, who slept in a soft bed. Important lords and ladies watched him day and night. But there was no talk about the other baby, Tom Canty, who lay in rags a few miles away.

Tom Canty was born one autumn day in London.
Edward Tudor was born on the same day.

♔

Let us move on nine years. London was fifteen hundred years old, and a great city – for that time. A hundred thousand people or more lived there. The streets were very narrow and dirty, and the houses were made of wood.

The Canty family lived in a small, old house in a very dirty street called Offal Court. Other terribly poor families lived there, too, and the Cantys had only one room. The mother and father had a bed in the corner; but Tom and his two sisters, Bet and Nan, slept on the floor.

Bet and Nan were kind girls, and their mother was like them. But their father was a terrible man. He was a thief and a beggar. Tom had to go begging every day, and when he came home with nothing, his father always hit him. But little Tom was not unhappy. His life was not unusual: all the fathers in Offal Court were bad to their children and hit them. At night, Tom's kind mother often brought him a piece of bread.

And then there was Old Andrew, too. He was a good old man, who liked to teach the children good ways. He taught Tom how to read and write, and told him stories about palaces and princes. Soon, Tom's head was full of these wonderful things. At night, he lay on the floor in his rags, tired and hungry; but in his dreams, he was a prince in a beautiful palace. He wanted only one thing:

to see a real prince. He thought about this all day and dreamed about it all night.

One morning, Tom got up hungry and walked through the streets. Soon, he was further away from home than ever before. He looked up and saw a wonderful building in front of him. It was the king's palace of Westminster.

'Perhaps I'll see a prince now,' he thought.

Soldiers stood in front of the gates, and people waited outside. They all wanted to see their king.

Poor little Tom, in his rags, was coming up to the gate when he saw something exciting. A young boy was coming out of the palace! There were servants all around him, and he wore gold and jewels on his clothes and hat. It was a real prince!

Tom put his face against the palace gates, but a soldier pushed him away, hurting his arm.

'Go away, beggar!' the soldier shouted. The crowd laughed; but the young prince was watching. He ran to the gate, and his face was hot and angry.

'DO NOT hurt that boy!' he shouted. 'Open the gates and bring him in.'

The soldier opened the gates, and Prince Edward Tudor, the king's son, shook Tom Canty's hand.

'You look hungry,' Prince Edward said. 'Come with me.'

Edward took Tom to a beautiful room in the palace, and told his servants to bring him food. And what food!

It was wonderful – just like the food in stories! Edward told the servants to go, and then he turned to Tom.

'What is your name, boy?'

'Tom Canty, sir.'

'And where do you live, Tom Canty?'

'In a poor street, sir – called Offal Court.'

'Do you have family?' asked Edward.

'Yes, sir,' replied Tom. 'I have a mother and two sisters. And a father, too, but he is not important to me – sorry for saying so.'

'Is he not kind to you?' Edward asked.

'Not to me or to anyone, sir,' Tom replied. 'He hits me.'

'Then tonight he shall be a prisoner in the Tower of London,' Edward said, angrily. 'My father will—'

'Please, sir,' said Tom. 'You forget that he is very poor. The Tower of London is only for important men.'

'That is true,' Edward said. 'Tell me, what do you do every day in this place, Offal Court?'

'I play with my friends,' explained Tom. 'We often sing and dance. In the summer, we swim in the river. We run and fight in the mud, too.'

'I would like to take off my shoes and play in the mud,' said Edward. 'Just once.'

'And I'd like to wear a prince's clothes,' replied Tom. 'Just once.'

'Then you shall,' said Edward. 'We shall change clothes!'

A few minutes later, Prince Edward was in rags, and Tom was wearing the prince's clothes. They stood and looked at themselves in a big mirror – and how strange it was! They looked just the same.

Edward laughed. 'We have the same hair, the same eyes, and the same face. Even our voices are the same!' He smiled at Tom. 'Who would know that you are not the prince?'

They looked at themselves in a big mirror –
and how strange it was! They looked just the same.

Edward took Tom's arm, but it was still hurting, and Tom gave a little cry.

'That soldier hurt you,' Edward said angrily.

'Oh, it is nothing—' Tom began, but the little prince was not listening.

'He did a terrible thing, and he will be sorry!' Edward said. He began to run out of the room, then stopped. He took a large ring that was lying on the table and went to put it in a cupboard. But he could not open the cupboard, so he put the ring under the carpet in the corner of the room, and then ran out to the gate, his face hot and his eyes angry.

'You – soldier. Come here!' Edward shouted. But the soldier hit him on the ear.

'Take that, beggar,' he shouted. 'That's because you got me in trouble with the prince earlier.'

'I *am* the prince,' said Edward. But the soldier looked at the little boy in rags and pulled him through the gates, then closed them.

'Go away, you stupid little beggar,' he said angrily.

'Open the gates at once!' Edward shouted. 'I am Prince Edward.' But the laughing crowd pushed him away and hit him.

'Make way,' they laughed. 'Here comes Prince Edward!'

CHAPTER 2

The Mad Prince

Inside the palace, Tom waited in the prince's room. He enjoyed himself at first. He looked at himself in the mirror, holding the prince's sword. He sat in each of the beautiful chairs in the room. But after half an hour, Tom began to worry.

'What will happen if somebody finds me here in these clothes?' Tom thought. 'The prince isn't here to explain. They will execute me for this!'

Just then, the door opened and a servant said, 'The Lady Jane Grey.'

'What's wrong, my prince?' said Edward's cousin when she came into the room and saw Tom's worried face.

'I... I am no prince,' he said. 'I'm only poor Tom Canty of Offal Court, a beggar boy. Please don't be angry with me. Bring me my rags, and I will go home.'

'Oh!' Lady Jane cried, afraid. 'What are you saying?' Then she turned and ran out of the room.

'There is no hope for me now,' thought Tom. 'Now they will come and take me.'

While Tom waited there, news travelled to every corner of the palace, from servant to servant and from lord to lady. 'The prince is mad,' people said. 'He thinks that he's a beggar!'

A while later, the doors of Edward's room opened and a servant came in.

'Your father, King Henry the Eighth, would like to see you,' the servant said.

Tom followed the servant through the palace, and important men, servants, and doctors walked with him.

At last, Tom arrived in a beautiful room, with the group of servants and lords. In front of him, a large and very fat man was sitting on a bed. His hair was grey, and his clothes, which looked expensive, were beautiful but old.

'Are you well, my son?' the man asked softly. Tom fell to the floor.

'Please don't hurt me, great king,' cried Tom. 'I am a poor boy. But I do not want to die.'

'Come to me,' King Henry said. 'You are not well.'

The king took Tom's face between his hands and looked lovingly into it. 'Do not be afraid,' he said. 'Don't you know your father?' Then he spoke to Tom in French.

'I do not know this language, sir,' said Tom.

Henry fell back onto the bed. 'Then it is true,' he cried. 'My son is mad!'

He held poor Tom's head in his arms. Then he sat up and looked at the people around him. His eyes were hard.

'My son is mad, but he will be better soon,' the king said. 'If anyone in the palace speaks of this, they will go to the Tower of London. My son *will* be the next King of England! We must sign all the papers to make him the Prince of Wales.'

'Sir,' said one of the lords. 'Only the Duke of Norfolk can sign these papers. And he is in the Tower of London.'

'Be silent!' the king cried. 'My son will not wait for that man! We will sign the papers ourselves – and you will execute the Duke of Norfolk!'

Little Tom's face went white, hearing this.

'You are very good to me, sir,' he said. 'But – but – I don't want anyone to die.'

'Don't worry about these things, my prince,' said the king. 'Now go to your room, and come back when you are better.'

When the servants took Tom back to his room, he walked slowly. This was not the palace of his dreams, he thought sadly. This was a prison made of gold.

Just after one o'clock, servants dressed Tom and took him to a beautiful room. There was a very large table in the room – and one chair! The plates and all the things on the table were gold – and there were servants all around the room. All the servants knew that the prince was not feeling well that day. So they did not look surprised when he ate with his fingers. And no one smiled when he looked at the vegetables on the table and asked, 'What are these? Can I eat them?'

'Our poor prince,' they said after the meal.

The servants did not look surprised when
the prince ate with his fingers.

That afternoon, King Henry the Eighth woke up after a
bad dream.

'I feel worse every day,' he thought. 'I will die soon.
But the Duke of Norfolk must die before me!' There was
a terrible look in his eyes.

'Execute Norfolk tomorrow,' he said when one of his
important lords, Hertford, arrived. 'Get the Great Seal.
Then I can sign the papers, and send him to his death!'

Lord Hertford looked down at the floor. 'You remember, sir...' he said quietly. 'You gave the Great Seal to Prince Edward two days ago.'

'Oh, yes, I did; I remember now. I forget so many things these days. Well, go and get it at once,' the king replied. 'Quick! Hurry!'

Lord Hertford hurried to Edward's rooms, but soon came back, with no seal.

'Sir,' Hertford told the king. 'I am very sorry, but the prince does not remember the seal. Shall I tell the servants to look in his room?'

'No. Do not worry the poor boy,' said the king sadly, and he lay back down on his bed.

That night, there was an important royal banquet for the prince at the Guildhall. At seven o'clock, servants came to dress Tom. By nine o'clock, there were fifty royal boats on the river in front of the palace. They had gold and silver decorations on them. Lights were burning in the palace gardens, and all along the River Thames, thousands of Londoners were waiting for their prince.

Slowly, great lords and ladies came through the palace gates and walked down to their boats. There was the sound of a trumpet, then a cry: 'Make way for Prince Edward!'

The crowds shouted when Tom appeared. He was wearing a coat of white, silver, gold, and jewels. Lady

Jane Grey and the prince's sister, Princess Elizabeth, walked slowly beside him, past the servants, to their boat.

While music played softly, the boats moved down the river. Their lights were like jewels on the water. To Princess Elizabeth and Lady Jane, this journey along the Thames was nothing special. But for Tom, born in rags in Offal Court, what a different world this was!

When the boats arrived, Tom, Princess Elizabeth, and Lady Jane rode horses to the Guildhall, and went to their seats at the banquet tables. Lords and ladies stood behind their chairs, waiting to help – and everyone in the room watched them! When Lord Hertford spoke quietly in Tom's ear, he stood up and drank from a gold cup. At once, the banquet began.

While music played softly, the boats moved down the river.

CHAPTER 3
Offal Court

Let us go back now, to that morning, and to poor little Prince Edward. The crowds who laughed at him outside the palace pushed him along, hitting him, and he was soon miles from his home. When he was alone at last, he looked around.

'I do not know this place,' he said to himself.

Edward had no shoes, and there were cuts on his feet. He stopped and washed them, then started to walk again.

He walked all day. He was hungry and cold, and there was blood on his face and hands. It was getting dark.

'I must find Offal Court,' Edward told himself. 'If I can find Tom's family, they will take me to the palace. They will explain to the soldiers that I am not their son. They will tell them that I am Prince Edward.'

At that minute, a big man took his arm from behind, shouting, 'There you are!' He was a hard, ugly man, and he was wearing rags.

'You haven't brought back any money, have you?' the man said. 'I'll hit you when we get home!'

Edward looked into the man's angry face. 'You are *his* father!' he cried.

'I'm *your* father,' John Canty shouted.

'I am too tired for this,' Edward replied. 'Take me to the king, my father, and you will be rich.'

'What? Are you mad?' Canty shouted. And he took
Edward's arm and pulled him down a narrow street and
into Offal Court. Edward fought and fought, but John
Canty was too strong for him.

'Stop that!' shouted Canty at last, and he held up a
big, heavy stick to hit the prince. Suddenly, an old man
caught Canty's arm.

'Are you trying to stop me?' Canty shouted at the
man. He hit him hard on the head with his stick, and the
man fell into the mud.

Canty held up a big, heavy stick to hit the prince.

A few minutes later, Edward and John Canty were in the Cantys' room. There was not much light, and it was a small, dirty place. Two girls and a woman were in a corner of the room.

'Now then,' Canty said to Edward, 'say your name – your real name – or you'll be sorry.'

'Do not tell *me* to speak,' said the little prince, and his face was red and angry. 'I am Prince Edward.'

Canty laughed, but his eyes were cold and hard.

The woman ran to Edward. 'My poor boy!' she cried. 'You read too many stories about princes!'

The prince looked into her face, and said softly: 'Your son is well and he is not mad, good lady. Take me to the palace, and the king will bring him to you.'

When he heard this, John Canty hit Edward hard on his back, and he fell into Mrs Canty's arms. She tried to move herself between the boy and John Canty, but Edward pulled himself away.

'Don't stop him,' Edward told her. 'Or he will hit you, too.'

Later that night, Edward lay on the floor, hurting terribly. Tom's mother softly touched his hair and cried.

'My father the king will thank you for this,' Edward told her. When she heard this, Tom's mother began to cry harder. Edward soon fell asleep, but Tom's mother lay worrying in her bed.

'He looks like my Tom, but there's something different about him,' she thought. 'How can I know that he is really my son?'

And then she remembered something. When Tom was surprised, he always put his hands in front of his eyes.

'I'll surprise the boy,' she thought, 'and see what happens.'

Tom's mother touched Edward, and he suddenly woke up and looked around him. But he did not move his hands. That night, she woke him up three times – but his hands never moved.

'Mad people can forget things,' she thought. 'But can their hands?'

That night, she woke him up three times –
but his hands never moved.

The Cantys only slept for a few hours. Later that night, a man knocked on their door.

'What is it?' John Canty shouted angrily.

'You hit Old Andrew in the street,' said a voice outside the door, 'and now he's dying.'

Canty's face went white. 'We have to leave this house!' he shouted at his family. 'Get up and run!'

Five minutes later, the Canty family and Edward were running for their lives through the streets of London.

'We can't go back to that house,' John Canty shouted at them. 'Never again.'

Canty held Edward's arm and pulled him along. The streets were dark, but when they arrived at the Thames, there were people and lights everywhere.

'Meet me later on London Bridge,' Canty told Tom's mother and sisters, before he lost them in the crowd. But he held onto Edward's hand.

'The people and lights are there for my banquet,' thought Edward. 'But how can there be a banquet without me?' Then he understood. Tom Canty was at the banquet! Tom Canty was taking his place!

Just then, a man walked into them, and for a second, Canty dropped Edward's hand. At once, Edward ran through the crowd and escaped.

'I will go to the Guildhall and tell everyone about that beggar,' Edward said to himself. 'He will die for this!'

CHAPTER 4

The Good Soldier

It was midnight by now, and inside the Guildhall, there was dancing. There were people wearing clothes from all around the world. Tom saw lords in yellow Russian coats, ladies in Moroccan green, and Turkish dancers in red and gold. Everything was like a wonderful dream for him.

But while he watched the colourful dancing inside, the real little prince was standing outside the gates of the Guildhall in rags.

'Let me in!' he shouted. 'I am Prince Edward.'

The crowd outside enjoyed this very much, of course, and they moved nearer to see the funny boy.

'Now hear me, you dogs!' the prince cried, with tears in his eyes. 'I am Prince Edward.'

'Prince or not, you are a brave boy,' a voice cried. 'And now you have a friend. I am Miles Hendon.' A tall, strong man pushed his way through the crowd and stood next to Edward. He was wearing soldier's clothes, and he had a sword.

'Kill him!' someone shouted, and at once the crowd pushed against him.

But Miles Hendon pulled out his sword, and fought wildly. Men fell here and there, but the crowd was strong. It was beginning to fight back when an officer shouted, 'Make way for the king's horses!'

'Now you have a friend. I am Miles Hendon.'

Soldiers rode straight through the crowd and up to the gates of the Guildhall. Everyone ran from the horses, and Miles Hendon took up the prince in his arms. They were soon far away.

Inside the Guildhall, there was the sound of a trumpet above the noise of the music and dancing, and at once, everyone was silent.

An officer shouted: 'The king is dead!'

For a while, everyone stood quietly. Then, they all looked at Tom. At last, there was a great shout.

'Long live the king!' everyone cried.

Tom's eyes moved across the crowd. Hundreds of faces were watching him. His people wanted to hear him speak. He said quietly to Hertford, 'If I tell the people to do something, will they do it?'

'Of course, sir,' replied Hertford. 'You are the king now. Your word is the law.'

Tom spoke in a loud, strong voice.

'There will be no more blood while I am king. Go to the Tower of London and tell the soldiers this: the king says that the Duke of Norfolk will not die.'

All around the room, there were loud cries.

'No more blood! Long live Edward the Sixth, King of England!'

'Long live the king!' everyone cried.

CHAPTER 5

Long Live the King

When they were free from the crowd outside the Guildhall, Miles and Edward ran through the streets and up to the river. There were more crowds at London Bridge, and poor Edward heard the news from a thousand voices at once.

'King Henry is dead!'

Tears came to his eyes. Most people were afraid of King Henry, but he was a kind and loving father to Edward. For a few seconds, Edward felt all alone in the world. Then he heard shouts of 'Long live King Edward the Sixth!'

'I am king now,' he thought, and it felt strange and wonderful.

Miles was taking Edward to an inn, where he had a room, but when they crossed the road to the inn, John Canty stopped them outside.

'You won't get away from me again,' he said, catching Edward. 'I'll hit you so hard.'

'Take your hands off him,' cried Miles. 'What is the boy to you?'

'It's none of *your* business, but he's my son,' answered Canty angrily.

'It is not true,' cried Edward. 'I will die before I go with him.'

Miles put his hand on his sword.

'Father or not, you shall not touch the boy,' he said. 'Or you will be very sorry.'

Canty walked away into the crowd, shouting angrily, and Miles took Edward into the inn. Up in Miles's room, the little king fell onto the bed. It was three o'clock in the morning, and he was tired.

'Wake me when my food is ready,' he told Miles, and then at once he fell asleep.

'Well!' laughed Miles. 'He comes to my room and takes my bed with no 'please' or 'thank you'! He calls himself a prince and he tries to live like one, too! Poor, mad little beggar – well, I will be his friend. I already like him, and the funny way that he talks. I will teach him, and watch over him.'

When Edward woke up, there was food on the table, and he sat down and began to eat.

'Bring me water,' he said.

Miles brought the prince a cup, then pulled a chair to the table, but before he could sit down, the boy said angrily: 'DO NOT SIT at the king's table!'

Miles nearly laughed, but he stopped himself. 'This mad boy will send me to the Tower next!' he thought, and he quietly stood and waited for Edward to finish his food.

'Tell me about yourself,' said Edward while he ate.

'I am the son of Sir Richard Hendon, of Hendon Hall,' Miles replied. 'Ten years ago, I went to France to

'DO NOT SIT at the king's table!'

fight in the king's army. But there I became a prisoner. A few months ago, I escaped from a French prison. I have just come back to England, and now I am going to Hendon Hall to see my family.'

'You will see your family soon,' said Edward. 'But I will never see my father again.' There were tears in his eyes. Then he told Miles about his life as a prince – and about how a beggar took his place.

'He's mad, but he tells a good story,' Miles thought.

Edward stopped talking and looked at Miles. 'Last night, you saved the King of England,' he said. 'You have been good to me, and now I shall do something for you. What would you like?'

Miles smiled. What could he ask from a mad boy? Then he thought of something. He was tired of standing.

'Please, sir,' he said, 'could I sit in the same room as the king?'

'Take a seat, Sir Miles Hendon,' replied Edward. 'From this day on, you will be *Sir* Miles Hendon. And *only you* will sit in the same room as the king.'

Miles sat down at once.

'I was right to ask him for that,' he thought. 'My legs hurt already – I wouldn't like to stand for weeks!'

Later that morning, while Edward slept, Miles went out to buy some clothes for him. But when he came back and opened the door of his room, it was empty. Miles ran downstairs.

'A boy brought a note from *you*, sir,' a servant told Miles. 'He was a tall boy with dark hair. And I gave the note to your friend. It said that you were waiting in Southwark. They left together.'

'I wrote no note, you stupid man!' Miles shouted. 'Was the boy alone?'

The servant thought for a second. 'He came alone, sir, but when they got outside, another man followed them.'

'It is that ugly villain who was waiting outside the inn!' Miles cried. 'My poor, mad little boy! I will find you!'

CHAPTER 6

A Kind King

When Tom woke up that same morning, he thought for one happy minute that he was at home again. Then he saw lords and servants standing around his bed, and he knew that he was still a prisoner and a king. They began to dress him. A very important lord gave a sock to the highest soldier in the army. The soldier gave it to a great officer of the Tower of London. Slowly, the sock moved through the hands of England's great and good. Finally, a servant carefully put the sock on Tom's foot. Then the second sock started its long journey to the king's bed.

When Tom was dressed at last, in beautiful purple clothes and a hat, one servant washed the royal face, and another dried it.

He ate breakfast, and then his great officers and a small army of servants took him to the Great Hall. There, with Lord Hertford at his side, he watched while the business of England went on before him. People came and went, reading long letters and bringing important papers, and every now and then Hertford touched Tom's arm and told him to sign something.

There was a lot of talk about money, and when Tom heard one of the officers say, 'The king has not paid his twelve hundred servants,' he suddenly sat up.

*Slowly, the sock moved through the hands
of England's great and good.*

'I don't need twelve hundred servants!' he cried. 'Let's
move to a smaller house, and…' But Hertford touched
his arm, and Tom stopped, his face red.

'I want to be outside in the fields and the sun,' poor Tom thought to himself. 'Why do they shut me up in here, and make me a king?' At last, Tom could not keep his eyes open any longer, and he fell asleep. At once, everyone stopped talking, and for a few minutes, while the young king slept, the business of England stopped!

The days went by, and the boring business of being king took most of Tom's time. Hertford told him what to do and what to say, and Tom tried not to make mistakes. Slowly, he became more comfortable in the palace. He still felt a little like a prisoner, but not all the time, and every day it was easier to be with the king's officers and servants.

On Tom's fourth day as king, he was looking out of a window when he saw a crowd near the gates. They were shouting and angry, and Tom was at once interested.

'Shall I send a servant down there, sir?' Lord Hertford asked. 'He can find out what it's all about.'

'Oh, yes, please!' said Tom excitedly.

A few seconds later, the servant came in with a group of officers. They were holding a man.

'The crowd was following this man, sir,' the servant said. 'He is on his way to the Tower, and the soldiers are executing him tomorrow.'

'I know this man,' Tom thought. 'This is the man who saved Giles Witt on New Year's morning when he fell in the river.'

'What is your crime?' Tom asked the prisoner.

'They say that I killed an old man with poison, sir.'

'He went into a house in Islington to visit a man who was ill, sir,' said one of the officers. 'And an hour later the man died.'

'And did they find poison in the dead man's room – or in this man's pocket?' Tom asked the officer.

'No, sir.'

'So we don't *know* that this man had poison – or that the old man really died of poisoning,' Tom said angrily, and then he turned to the prisoner. 'What do you say?' he asked.

'I was not in Islington that day,' the man said. 'I was not taking a life, I was saving one. I saved a boy who fell in the river.'

'When did the crime happen?' Tom asked an officer.

'On New Year's morning, sir.'

'Stand up and go,' Tom told the prisoner. 'You are free.'

When Tom turned to the officers, his face was red. 'Why were you sending this man to the Tower?' he said. 'You found no poison, so you do not know that he killed anybody.'

'They say that our king is mad,' one of the lords in the room said quietly to another. 'But he does not sound mad to me.'

CHAPTER 7
The Gang of Thieves

Let us go back a few days to see the real king, Edward.
He was in Southwark with the tall, dark-haired boy
who came for him at the inn, and he was sitting down
angrily by the road.

'You said that Sir Miles Hendon was waiting for us
here,' he said. 'I will stop here and walk no more. He
must come to me.'

'He can't. He's hurt,' said the boy.

'Hurt? Why didn't you say? Then we must go to him
at once,' said Edward, and he followed the boy along a
road and at last into some woods. After a while, they
came to an old barn, and Edward followed the boy
inside. There was no one there.

Edward looked at the boy. 'Where is Miles?' he asked,
but the boy only laughed. Then John Canty appeared.

'Where are your sisters and mother?' he shouted angrily.

'My mother is dead,' Edward replied. 'And my sisters
are in the palace – *my* palace.'

The boy laughed, but Canty said, 'I don't want to
hear any more of this, or you will be sorry. Now come
here, Hugo. I need to talk to you.'

While John Canty talked quietly with the boy, Edward
sat in a corner of the barn. He thought sadly of his father,
and remembering happy times with him, he began to cry.

Soon, the tired, lonely king was asleep.

When Edward woke up, it was dark. A fire was burning at the other end of the barn, and he could see men and women sitting around it. They were terrible to see: some had only one hand, one leg, or one eye; others had burns on their faces; and all were dirty and looked like villains. They were finishing their meal, and now they began to laugh, sing, and talk.

They were thieves, beggars, and killers. Edward listened to them, and they began to tell their stories.

'I was a farmer,' one man said. 'I had a wife and three children. My mother took care of ill people in our village, but one day, an old man died. His family said that my mother killed him.'

There were tears in the old farmer's eyes. 'They said that she was a murderer, so soldiers came and killed her. They took our farm, so we walked from town to town and begged for bread. But we cannot beg in England, can we? They caught my wife and killed her. And when they caught me, they cut off my ears. But I didn't stop begging – what could I do? There was nothing for the children to eat, so they died, too. And when they catch me for begging again, they'll execute me.'

Edward stood up. 'They shall not execute you,' he cried. 'I will stop them!'

Everyone turned and looked at Edward. 'And who are you?' they laughed.

'I am Edward, King of England,' he said.

The thieves laughed wildly.

'Be careful,' said a man with burns on his face. 'If the king's officers hear you saying that, they will kill you.'

'Let's call him "Foo Foo the First, King of the Moon",' a woman said, and everyone laughed.

'Long live King Foo Foo!' the thieves cried, and they took Edward's arms, sat him on a throne of boxes, and put a plate on his head as a crown.

'Be kind to us, King Foo Foo,' they cried, laughing. 'Let us be your servants!'

'I tried to be kind,' Edward thought, tears running down his face. 'But this is how they thank me.'

'Long live King Foo Foo!' the thieves cried.

The next morning, the gang left the woods and walked east. They shouted at people on the road, and they stole things from farm houses, but nobody tried to stop them: they were too afraid. Early in the afternoon, they came to a village, and the gang went away in small groups to beg or steal. Hugo went with Edward.

'There is nothing to steal,' Hugo told Edward, after watching the village for a while. 'We will have to beg.'

'I will not beg or steal,' said Edward.

'Your father says that you have begged on the streets of London all your life!'

'Do not be so stupid!' replied Edward.

'Now listen,' said Hugo. 'When I fall down, ask that man for help. Say that I am ill and that you are my brother. He looks kind, and he will give us money.'

When the man came near them, Hugo fell to the ground. He lay in the mud and turned this way and that.

'Two pence for food, sir,' he cried. 'I am ill.'

'Poor boy, you shall have three pence,' the man said.

'He is not ill. He is a beggar and a thief!' said Edward. 'He has taken your three pence, and money from your pocket, too!'

Hugo jumped to his feet and ran, and the man followed after him, shouting and calling for help. Edward knew that he could escape at last, and he turned and ran the other way, as fast as he could.

CHAPTER 8
Edward's Escape

Edward ran away from Hugo to the other side of the village, and only stopped running when the houses were far behind. He walked for a few more hours, and then, feeling hungry and tired, he stopped at a farm house to ask for help.

'Go away, beggar,' the farmer shouted when he saw Edward's rags. 'Go away, or we'll call the constable.'

Edward walked across fields and then into a wood. He thought that he would go through the wood and find a road, but he only went deeper and deeper into it. He walked and walked, but it began to get dark, and Edward was afraid. He did not want to spend the night in this dark, lonely wood.

How pleased he was, then, when at last he saw a light, and came to a small stone house. He walked up to a window, looked inside, and saw a small room with a fire and a bed. An old man in rags was sitting by the fire, and he looked up and came to the door.

'Come in! It's cold outside,' he said. 'Who are you?'

'I am the king,' Edward replied.

'Come in, King!' the old man said. 'Sit down.'

The old man put wood on the fire, and brought a chair near to it for Edward. He had wild eyes, and all the time he talked quietly to himself.

He washed the cuts on Edward's feet, and then began to cook some food. The old man gave Edward some dinner, and then he took him into another room, and made a warm, comfortable bed for him.

'So, you're a king?' he said, smiling. 'Of which country?'

'Of England. My father was King Henry the Eighth.'

The man's face darkened, and he was still for a minute.

'Do you know that he took my house from me, and from others?' he said at last.

But there was no answer. When the old man looked down at Edward, he was asleep.

The old man moved around the house, looking for something here and there. Sometimes he stopped to listen, and looked at the bed, talking quietly to himself all the time. At last, he found what he wanted. It was an old knife, and he sat by the fire and looked at it.

'So it was his father who did those terrible things!' he said to himself.

The old man took some pieces of rag, and slowly, carefully, he tied Edward to the bed.

'King Henry took my house,' he said to himself. 'Now I will take his son.'

When Edward woke up the next morning, he could not move. He opened his eyes and saw the old man. He was sitting on the bed with a long knife in his hand.

The old man was sitting on the bed.

Poor Edward tried to pull his arms and legs free, but he could not move them. He tried to shout, but there was a rag around his mouth.

'It's time to die, son of Henry!' the man said. Then he stood up and held the knife above Edward's head.

At that minute, someone knocked on the door. The knife fell from the old man's hand and he pulled some rags over the boy, shaking.

'Open the door!' a voice called outside, and the sound was like music to Edward's ears. It was Miles's voice.

'I am looking for a boy,' Miles told the old man when he opened the door. 'A poor boy in rags. I know that he went to the farm on the other side of the wood, not far from here.'

Edward tried to call to Miles, but he could make no sound with the rag around his mouth. He pulled and pulled at the rags that tied him to the bed, but he could not move them.

'A poor boy came here last night,' the old man told Miles. 'I gave him some food, and then he left. He went that way. Come – I will show you.'

Edward listened while the two men went outside. All his hopes died when they walked away, and tears ran down his face.

'My only friend has gone,' thought Edward. 'The old man will come back soon, and...'

Then, the door opened. Edward closed his eyes. He thought that he could feel the knife at his neck, and he opened his eyes again. But it was John Canty and Hugo!

How happy Edward was, at that minute, to see those two villains! A minute or two later, his arms and legs were free, and Canty and Hugo were running with him through the wood.

CHAPTER 9
The Meat Thief

A nd so Edward was back in the gang of thieves again. He did not beg or steal for them, and every day he tried to escape from this terrible life of crime. At night, in his dreams, he was back in his palace.

Most of the gang were not unkind to 'King Foo Foo', but it was Hugo's job to watch Edward – and Hugo did not like him. Hugo was always looking for a way to make trouble for the little king.

One morning, he and Edward went into a small town and walked past a woman who was carrying a big bag of meat.

Hugo ran up behind the woman and took the bag, then dropped it into Edward's arms.

'Take it!' he shouted, and he ran away.

Edward dropped the bag at once, but the woman caught his arm.

'Thief!' she cried.

'Take your hands off me, woman,' Edward said. 'I did not steal your bag.' But a crowd of angry people were standing around him.

'We'll teach you a lesson,' a big man said, holding a long piece of wood above his head.

But just then, a sword came down softly on the man's arm, and a voice called out, 'Good people, go carefully.

Hugo ran up behind the woman and took the bag.

Let's ask a judge to decide about this – not you.'

The circle of people slowly opened, the woman dropped Edward's arm, and Edward ran happily to the man with the sword.

'Miles!' he cried. 'You have saved me again!'

Miles smiled, and then said quietly to Edward, 'Listen to me and say nothing.'

A constable soon appeared, and Miles, Edward, the woman, and the crowd followed him to the court.

'Did this boy steal from you?' the judge asked the woman, when the group sat in the town's court room that afternoon.

'Yes, sir,' she replied. 'He stole some meat.'

'And how much did the meat cost you?'

'I paid forty-four pence for it.'

The judge's eyes darkened, and Miles's face turned white. But poor Edward, who did not know the country's laws about stealing, waited quietly.

'Leave us,' the judge told the other people in the room. Then he turned to the woman.

'Good woman,' he said, 'this poor boy only stole because he was hungry. But the law says that I must execute a thief if he steals more than thirteen pence.'

Edward jumped up, his eyes open wide; but the woman began to shake, and cried out:

'Oh, no! I don't want that!'

'I have not written the cost of the meat in my book yet,' the judge said, and he looked hard at her. 'Are you sure of the cost?'

'Oh… no… yes… I remember now,' she answered. 'I paid eight pence for it.'

When he heard this, Miles Hendon jumped happily to his feet and put his arms around Edward. The woman left with her meat, but she was not alone. The constable went after her into the hall outside, and Miles, who saw everything, followed them.

'It's a good piece of meat,' the constable was saying to the woman. 'I will buy it from you for eight pence.'

'You will not!' said the woman. 'I paid forty-four pence for it.'

'But in court just now you said that it cost only eight pence. Let's go back now and tell the judge. Then they will execute that boy!'

'No, no!' the woman cried. 'Here you are. Give me eight pence, and say no more, I beg you.'

The woman gave the meat to the constable and walked away crying, while the constable hid the meat behind a chair and then went back into the court room.

'You will go to prison for two weeks,' the judge was telling Edward when Miles arrived back at his side.

Edward's mouth fell open.

'Say nothing, and do what I say,' Miles said quietly.

It was nearly the end of the day, and the streets were

empty when Edward and Miles followed the constable through the town to the prison.

'Look away,' Hendon suddenly said to the constable. 'Then this poor boy can escape.'

'What did you say?' said the constable. 'Shall I send you to prison, too?'

'I saw what happened with that woman outside the court room,' said Miles. 'You only paid her eight pence for that meat. The king's officers will execute you for that! And I'm going to tell them now!'

He turned to go, but the constable took his arm.

'No, no! Please, dear sir. Go now with the boy, and I will look away and see nothing.'

'Good,' said Miles. 'And you will give the woman back her meat?'

'Yes,' said the constable.

'Don't forget!' Miles said, and he and Edward turned and ran away down the road and out of the town.

While they ran, they talked about their adventures of the last few days.

'We must go at once to see Lord Hertford, Miles,' Edward said. 'I have to win back the throne!'

'His poor little head is still busy with this mad dream,' Miles thought to himself. 'But I have things to do in London before I go to Hendon Hall – so to London we will go!'

CHAPTER 10

Coronation

While England's real king was going around the country wearing rags, eating very little, and running away from thieves and murderers, King Tom Canty was beginning to enjoy himself.

He did not make many mistakes now. When he wanted to talk to Princess Elizabeth or Lady Jane Grey, he called for them, and when he was bored, he sent them away. He loved the royal banquets, and liked walking to dinner with an army of officers and servants. He liked his wonderful clothes, and asked for more – and he had more servants now than King Henry! He was still a kind king, and he changed many laws to help poor people, but when he was angry, his lords and officers were very afraid.

At first, Tom felt very sorry for Edward, the real king. But his new life was exciting. He did not think about Edward very often now, and he began to forget his family, too.

On the evening of the nineteenth of February, 1547, Tom fell asleep in his comfortable bed in the palace feeling happy. The next day was the day of the coronation.

That same evening, Edward and Miles arrived at London Bridge. Everybody was talking about the coronation, and people were eating, drinking, and dancing in the streets. Edward lost Miles in the crowds and walked on to Westminster Abbey. There, he watched while workmen carried things in and out of the building, making it ready for the next day.

'That beggar will not wear my crown,' Edward thought. When no one was looking, he ran into the abbey and hid behind some decorations. When the last workman left the abbey that night, he was asleep on the floor in the corner.

At seven the next morning, Tom rode a beautiful white horse through London to Westminster Abbey. Hertford was next to him, and many lords and servants followed. The streets were full of people and colourful decorations. Music played, and people danced and sang. There were faces at every window, and crowds in every street.

'Long live the king!' they shouted.

One of the people in the crowd was Tom's mother, and when he saw her, in his surprise, his hands flew up in front of his eyes. His mother saw it, and she pushed to the front of the crowd.

'My son, my child,' she cried, touching his leg.

An officer pushed her away, and Tom looked down at her and said, 'I don't know you, woman.'

Tom rode on through the crowds, but he did not see them any more, or hear their shouts. He could only think of his mother's sad face.

At nine, the people inside the abbey heard the sound of guns – the king was outside! They sat and waited quietly.

A trumpet played, and the king's soldiers walked into the abbey. Then Tom appeared in his beautiful gold coronation clothes. Music played while great lords and high officers slowly walked with Tom to the throne. Then, the coronation began. But every minute, Tom's face became whiter, and there was a sad look in his eyes.

At last, the highest lord in the country was holding the crown of England above Tom's head. Everyone went quiet, but in that important minute, a boy began to run through the abbey.

A boy with no shoes, wearing rags, who held his hand up and cried out: 'Do not put the crown of England on that boy's head. I am the king.'

Soldiers and officers hurried to catch the boy, but at the same time, Tom Canty, in his royal clothes, shouted:

'Do not touch him! He *is* the king.'

There was not a sound in the abbey. Everyone looked at Tom.

'The king is not well,' Hertford quietly told one of the king's officers. 'Take that beggar away.'

'Do not touch him, he is the king!' Tom said again.

Edward came to the throne, and a look of surprise fell across the faces of everyone in the abbey. They were all thinking the same thing: 'That beggar looks like the king!'

For a minute, nobody spoke. Then, Hertford turned to Edward.

*'Do not put the crown of England
on that boy's head. I am the king.'*

'Will you please answer some questions?' he asked.

'Of course,' said Edward. Hertford asked him many questions about the palace, and Edward replied at once. No one could understand it. How did this beggar know so much about the palace?

'Your answers are right,' said Hertford, looking at Edward. 'If you can tell me one more thing, we will know that you are the king... Where is the Great Seal?'

'I keep it in the small cupboard in my room,' Edward answered easily.

'Go to this place and bring the seal,' Hertford told one of the king's officers.

The officer turned and left. Then all the great lords and ladies in the abbey sat and waited. They looked from one boy to the other, and talked.

When the officer came back, everyone watched silently while he walked to the front of the abbey, then spoke to Hertford.

'The seal is not there,' Hertford said, turning to Edward. 'Soldiers, put this boy out into the street.'

'Do not touch him, or you will pay with your life!' shouted Tom, angrily.

'Did you look carefully for the seal?' Hertford asked the officer. 'That big gold ring can change the throne of England.'

'The seal is a big gold ring?' cried Tom, jumping to his feet. 'Now I know what it is – and where it is, too.

But I did not put it there.' He turned to Edward. 'Do you remember, sir? After we changed clothes in your room, you went to talk to the soldier at the gates. But before you left, you hid the seal. You could not open the cupboard, so...?'

A smile appeared on Edward's face. 'Now I remember! I put it under the carpet in the corner of my room!'

The officer rode away to the palace again, and inside the abbey, people stood, waited, and talked excitedly. The minutes came and went. At last, the officer ran into the abbey. He was holding the Great Seal! A great shout went up through the abbey:

'Long live the true king!'

The abbey was full of the sounds of happy shouts and trumpets. Edward stood in his rags, smiling happily.

'Take the boy to the Tower,' said Hertford, taking Tom's arm. But Edward stopped them.

'Do not hurt him,' he said. 'I have won my crown again. He helped me, and no one must touch him.'

Servants carefully took Tom's gold clothes and dressed Edward, and then the coronation began again. England had its true king at last, and guns sent the news across the city of London.

CHAPTER 11

The Pauper King

Miles Hendon walked for hours through the dirtiest, poorest streets of London, but he could not find Edward. He decided to rest for a while by the Thames, but after he heard the coronation guns, he fell asleep. He did not wake up until the next morning.

'My poor, mad boy will go to the palace,' he thought when he woke, remembering the guns. So he stood up and began to walk there.

Just before eleven o'clock, Miles arrived at the palace. When he walked up to the gates, a soldier looked at him carefully.

'Are you Sir Miles Hendon?' the soldier asked.

'I am Miles Hendon, but not a "Sir",' he replied.

'Follow me, please,' said the soldier. 'The king would like to see you.'

'What have I done? Why does the king want to see me?' worried Miles, following the soldier through the palace.

At last, they came to the Great Hall. Miles took off his hat and followed the soldier to the throne. He was afraid, but then the king moved his head, and Miles saw his face.

'It is not possible!' he thought. His poor, mad boy was sitting on the throne of England!

'I'm dreaming,' Miles told himself. But his little pauper friend looked real, and the other people in the room looked real, too. How could he find out if this really was his beggar boy? Then Miles thought of something. He took a chair and sat down. At once, he heard angry voices, and a hand took his arm.

'Stand up, you stupid man,' a voice shouted. 'Nobody sits in front of the king!'

But Edward suddenly stood up.

'Do not touch him!' he cried. 'This man is my true servant, and he saved my life with his sword. For that, he became Sir Miles Hendon. Sir Miles – and *only* Sir Miles – can sit in front of the king. And his children, and their children, and their children, can do the same!'

'Then it is my pauper! My little beggar boy!' cried Miles.

'My soldiers found you!' said Edward. 'I knew that you would come to the palace looking for me, and I described you to them.'

There was a noise at the other end of the room, and a servant brought Tom into the Great Hall. Edward turned from Miles to Tom.

'I have heard that you were a good and kind king, and I am pleased with you,' said Edward. 'We will take care of your mother and sisters, and from this day you shall be Sir Tom. Then everyone will remember that you were once a king.'

The servants took Tom from the room, and, pleased and happy, he ran to tell his mother the good news.

And so we leave King Edward in his great palace. Poor Edward did not live for many years, but he tried to help his people while he was king. He found the judge who saved him when Hugo stole the meat, and helped him to become an important man. He found the poor farmer, too, saved him from the gang of thieves, and gave him a comfortable life. Under Edward, many beggars and thieves escaped execution, and many laws changed.

More than once, some great lord said to Edward, 'Our laws are already kind to the poor, sir. You do not need to change them.'

And every time, Edward looked at the lord and said, 'What do you know about life as a pauper? My people and I know, but you do not.'

King Edward liked to tell the story of his adventures, and of how he nearly missed the coronation because he was sleeping so deeply on the floor in a corner of Westminster Abbey.

He was friends with Tom Canty and Miles Hendon for the rest of his short life. Miles went home to Hendon Hall and soon married. Tom lived a long and happy life, and his mother and sisters did, too – but nobody ever saw John Canty again.

Everyone knew that Tom Canty was Sir Tom, and they stopped when they saw him in the street.

'That man was once a king,' they said. 'Take off your hat to him.'

'That man was once a king,' they said.

GLOSSARY

appear *(v)* to suddenly be seen

banquet *(n)* a special dinner for a large number of people

barn *(n)* a large building on a farm; the farmer keeps food or animals in it

become (past tense **became**) *(v)* to begin to be something

beggar *(n)* a person who asks other people for money or food

city *(n)* a big and important town

constable *(n)* a policeman or policewoman

coronation *(n)* when somebody is made a king or queen

court *(n)* In a court, a judge or a group of people (called a jury) decide if a person has done something wrong, and what will happen to them.

cousin *(n)* the child of your aunt or uncle

crime *(n)* something that somebody does that is against the law

crown *(n)* a circle made of gold and beautiful stones (called jewels) that a king/queen wears on his/her head

cut off *(v)* to take one piece from something bigger using a knife

decoration *(n)* a beautiful thing that you add to something to make it look nicer

execute *(v)* to kill a person; **execution** *(n)*

farm *(n)* People keep animals and grow fruit and vegetables on a farm.

farmer *(n)* a person who has got a farm

gang *(n)* a group of people who break the law

gate *(n)* a thing like a door in a wall or outside a building, that someone can go through

hall *(n)* a big room or building used for meetings

inn *(n)* a place like a hotel, but smaller

jewel *(n)* a beautiful stone that is very expensive

judge *(n)* the person who decides what will happen to a criminal

lady *(n)* a name for an important woman who is usually rich; a nice way of saying 'woman'

law *(n)* a law says what people can or cannot do in a country

lord *(n)* a name for an important man who is usually rich

mad *(adj)* ill in your head

make way to move out of the way

mud *(n)* ground that is soft, wet, and brown

officer *(n)* a person who does important work, sometimes for a king or queen

palace *(n)* a very large house for a king or queen

pauper *(n)* a very poor person

poison *(n)* If you eat or drink poison, you will become very ill.

prince *(n)* a man in a royal family, usually the son of a king or queen

rags *(n)* clothes that are very old and dirty

royal *(adj)* a king or queen, or anything they have

sad *(adj)* unhappy

save *(v)* to take somebody or something away from danger

servant *(n)* a person who works in another person's house, doing work like cooking and cleaning

sign *(v)* to write your name on something

Sir *(n)* a name for an important man

sword *(n)* a very long knife that people use for fighting

take care (of somebody) *(v)* to help somebody

tear *(n)* a drop of water that comes from your eye when you cry

throne *(n)* a special chair for a king or queen

tie *(v)* to close or put together two parts of something

trumpet *(n)* a musical instrument that is made of metal; you put your mouth on the end and blow into it

ugly *(adj)* not nice to look at

villain *(n)* a bad person, usually in a book or film

STORY NOTES

Duke of Norfolk an important lord; King Henry the Eighth put him in prison in 1546 for crimes against the crown

the Guildhall a very big and beautiful room in London; the city's most important people met there

Great Seal a big gold ring which the king used to close letters and put a royal picture on them

Henry the Eighth King of England from 1509–1547

Islington (in the 1500s) a village outside London

London Bridge the only bridge across the River Thames in the 1500s; there were shops and houses on the bridge, and always crowds of people and horses

Palace of Westminster an important royal house, and Henry's favourite home; it had 1,500 rooms and was as big as a small town

Prince of Wales the oldest son of the king or queen of the United Kingdom usually has this name; being the Prince of Wales is also an important job

River Thames an important river that goes through London

Southwark a place south of London Bridge

Tower of London a big building next to the River Thames; Henry kept important prisoners there

Westminster Abbey a big and very important building in London; many of England's kings and queens had their coronations there

ABOUT TUDOR ENGLAND

The kings and queens of England and Wales between 1485 and 1603 were from a family called the Tudors. We call that time 'Tudor England'.

Henry the Eighth and Edward the Sixth

Henry the Eighth was the second Tudor king, and he came to the throne in 1509. Henry made very big changes in England, and because of this – and also because he married six times – he had many enemies. He executed thousands of people, and two of them were his wives. When he died in 1547, his son Edward became king. Edward was the son of Henry's third wife, Jane Seymour, who died soon after Edward was born. Edward only lived until he was fifteen, and Henry's daughters Mary and Elizabeth then came to the throne.

Henry the Eighth

London

In Tudor times, most people lived in the countryside. London was the biggest city in England, but it was still small – it only took twenty minutes to walk from the city centre to the countryside. Life in London was hard: the streets were very crowded, narrow, and dirty, there was lots of crime, and many people were often very ill.

The rich and the poor

In Tudor times, life was very different for rich people and poor people. Rich people lived in big houses in the countryside, with beautiful gardens. Their children went to school, and they enjoyed country sports, dancing, and games like tennis. Poor people had to beg, steal, or die. In some places, about a quarter of all people were beggars.

Crime and punishment

When people broke the law, there were often very hard punishments for them. There was a beating and sometimes execution for stealing, and constables whipped beggars. Many people came to watch executions, and they sometimes brought their children. Executions were often beheadings – when the executioner cuts off the person's head.

---

beating *(n)* hitting someone again and again

countryside *(n)* a place with fields, woods, farms, etc., that is away from towns and cities

punishment *(n)* hurting someone because they have done something wrong

whip *(v)* to hit an animal or a person with something

ABOUT MARK TWAIN

Mark Twain's real name was Samuel Clemens. He was born in Florida, a town in Missouri, USA, in 1835 and his family then moved to Hannibal, Missouri.

After he left school, he went to work for a few different newspapers, and soon began to write pieces for them. From 1857 to 1861, he was a river-pilot, taking river boats down the great Mississippi river. The name 'Mark Twain' came from his life on the Mississippi. When sailors shouted 'Mark Twain', the river-pilot knew that there were four metres of water under the boat.

People first heard about Mark Twain when he wrote a short story for a newspaper in 1865, and he was soon famous for his funny, clever writing. He wrote *The Adventures of Tom Sawyer* in 1876, *The Prince and the Pauper* in 1881, and *Adventures of Huckleberry Finn* in 1884.

In 1891, Mark Twain moved to Europe with his wife and three children, and began to travel a lot. He gave many talks about his work. But the later years of his life were often difficult and unhappy: his wife and two of his daughters died, he often had money problems, and he began to feel angry about many things in the world.

Mark Twain died in 1910. He wrote twenty-eight books and many short stories, and is one of the most famous American writers of all time.

ACTIVITIES

Before Reading

1 Match the words to the definitions.

1 king   a very old clothes

2 pauper   b a long knife that people fight with

3 soldier   c the most important person in a country

4 rags   d a big dinner for important people

5 banquet   e someone who fights in an army

6 sword   f someone who has no money

2 Look at the cover and the title of the book. Tick (✓) three things that you think will happen in the story.

1 A pauper will live in a palace. ☐

2 A prince will save a pauper's life. ☐

3 A prince and a pauper will change clothes. ☐

4 A pauper will travel to another country. ☐

5 A prince and a pauper will become friends. ☐

3 Look at the front and back cover, and the chapter titles. Then answer the questions.

1 Who wrote *The Prince and the Pauper*?

2 When and where does the story happen?

3 What is special about the prince and the pauper?

4 Do you think the story will have a happy ending?

ACTIVITIES

While Reading

Read Chapter 1. Tick (✓) the people who are kind to Tom.

1 Bet and Nana ☐
2 Tom's father ☐
3 Tom's mother ☐
4 a soldier ☐
5 Edward ☐

Read Chapter 2. Then write the names of the characters.

1 _____ does not come back to his room.
2 _____ asks for his rags.
3 _____ runs out of Edward's room.
4 _____ thinks that his son is mad.
5 _____ is in the Tower of London.
6 _____ looks for the Great Seal.

Read Chapter 3. Are the sentences true (T) or false (F)?

1 Edward can go back to the palace. _____
2 Edward meets John Canty in the street. _____
3 In Offal Court, a man hits John Canty. _____
4 Tom's mother knows that the boy is her son. _____
5 Tom Canty is at the banquet. _____

Read Chapter 4. Write *Tom, Edward*, or *Miles*.

Who…

1 watches some dancers?   _____
2 cannot go into the Guildhall?   _____
3 thinks that Edward is brave?   _____
4 meets someone in soldier's clothes?   _____
5 asks Lord Hertford an important question?   _____

Read Chapter 5. Then put the events in order.

a Miles meets John Canty.   _____
b A tall boy comes to the inn.   _____
c Miles goes out to buy some clothes.   _____
d Miles tells Edward about himself.   _____
e Miles and Edward go to London Bridge.   _____
f Edward hears news about his father.   _____

Read Chapter 6. Choose the correct words to complete the sentences.

1 Tom says that he does not need twelve hundred *soldiers* / *servants*.
2 The business of England stops when Tom *speaks* / *falls asleep*.
3 Tom becomes more *comfortable* / *unhappy* with life in the palace.
4 One day, he meets the man who *killed* / *saved* Giles Witt.
5 Tom says that the man is *free* / *mad*.

Read Chapter 7. Are the sentences true (T) or false (F)?

1 Miles takes Edward to Southwark. _____

2 A soldier tells his story to the gang of thieves. _____

3 You cannot beg in England. _____

4 Hugo tells a man that he is ill. _____

5 Edward tries to steal some money. _____

6 Edward runs away. _____

Read Chapter 8. Correct the <u>underlined</u> word in each sentence to make the sentences true.

1 Edward does not want to sleep in a <u>village</u>.

2 Edward meets an old man with <u>kind</u> eyes.

3 He tells the man that he's the <u>prince</u>.

4 When Edward wakes up, he cannot <u>see</u>.

5 The man has a long <u>stick</u> in his hand.

6 Edward hears <u>Tom's</u> voice outside.

Read Chapter 9. Then complete the sentences with numbers.

1 The woman paid _____ pence for the meat.

2 The judge must execute a thief if he steals more than _____ pence.

3 The constable buys the meat for _____ pence.

4 Edward will go to prison for _____ weeks.

Read Chapter 10. Which three sentences are true? Tick the three true sentences.

1 Tom helps poor people when he is king.   ☐
2 Tom thinks about Edward and his family all the time. ☐
3 The king's officers try to catch Edward in the abbey,
   but Tom stops them.   ☐
4 An officer finds something important under a carpet. ☐
5 Edward wants to send Tom to the Tower of London.   ☐
6 The coronation never happens.   ☐

Read Chapter 11. Then complete the sentences with one word or name.

Edward…
1 describes _____ to his soldiers.
2 takes care of _____ family.
3 finds the _____ who helped him when Hugo stole the
   meat.
4 saves many beggars from _____.
5 is a good king because he knows about life as a _____.

ACTIVITIES

After Reading

Vocabulary

1 **Unscramble the words to complete the sentences.**

1 Tom is a poor _____ (gebgar).
2 His father, John Canty, is a terrible _____ (llanivi).
3 Tom first sees the prince when he's outside the palace _____ (staeg).
4 King Henry the Eighth wants to _____ (ecutexe) the Duke of Norfolk.
5 Tom goes to a (quatben) _____ at the Guildhall.

2 **Match the words to the definitions.**

inn law save sign tears

1 These go down your face when you cry. _____
2 People stay in rooms in this place. _____
3 To write your name on something important. _____
4 It tells you what you must or must not do. _____
5 You do this to someone when you stop something bad happening to them. _____

3 **Decide if each word is a person or a thing.**

*constable decoration farmer jewel
judge lord poison seal servant sword*

Grammar

1 Complete the paragraph with *the*, *some*, or *any*.

Hugo tried to steal ¹_____ money from a man in the village, but Edward told ²_____ man that Hugo was a thief. After Edward escaped from ³_____ village, he walked for hours and hours. Poor Edward was cold and hungry, but he could not get ⁴_____ help or find ⁵_____ food. Finally, Edward walked into ⁶_____ woods. After ⁷_____ time, he saw a little stone house. He knocked on ⁸_____ door, and an old man opened it. ⁹_____ man gave Edward ¹⁰_____ food.

2 It is the night before the coronation. Complete Edward's thoughts with *will* or *won't* and the verbs below.

hide   listen   see   stop   wear

1 I _____ behind those decorations.
2 The workmen _____ me there.
3 I _____ the coronation.
4 That beggar _____ the crown of England!
5 I'm afraid. Perhaps they _____ to me.

Reading

1 Put the events of the entire story in order.

a Edward hides in Westminster Abbey. _____

b John Canty takes Edward to Offal Court. _____

c An old man ties Edward to a bed. _____

d Tom and Edward change clothes. _____

e Edward hears that his father is dead. _____

f Hugo takes Edward to meet the gang of thieves. _____

g Tom walks to Westminster Palace and
sees Edward. _____

h Miles saves Edward outside the Guildhall. _____

i A soldier pushes Edward out of the palace gates. _____

2 Match the people to the things that they do in the story.

*Edward   John Canty   King Henry the Eighth
Lord Hertford   Miles   Tom*

Who...

1 hits a man and kills him? _____

2 wants to execute a man in the Tower of London? _____

3 fights with a crowd outside the Guildhall? _____

4 saves a prisoner from execution? _____

5 asks Edward for the Great Seal? _____

6 escapes from the gang of thieves? _____

Writing

1 Read the paragraph. Then answer the questions.

> We left that terrible, dirty house because Tom's father
> killed someone. The villain pulled me through the streets
> of London, but for a minute, he dropped my arm. I ran
> away through the crowd, and he couldn't find me. Now
> I'm going to the Guildhall. It's the night of my banquet,
> and that beggar boy is there in my place!

1 Who is telling the story?
2 Who is 'the villain' and who is 'that beggar boy'?
3 What tenses are there in the text?
4 What happens immediately after this?

**2 You are Tom, and you are sitting at the banquet at the
    Guildhall. Write a paragraph to describe...**

– the journey along the river.
– what you are wearing.
– what is happening in the Guildhall.
– how you are feeling.

**3 Now choose another person from the story. Write a
    paragraph about another part of the story.**

Speaking

1 Put the words in the correct order to make sentences.

1 reading really I book the enjoyed
2 changed when I the scene loved Tom Edward and clothes
3 character Miles Hendon my was favourite
4 I like the man's old house didn't bit the in
5 ending the exciting I found really
6 funny think the story was very I

2 Underline the words and phrases in exercise 1 that…

- express feelings and give opinions.
- identify a part of the story.

3 Discuss the sentences in exercise 1. Which do you agree with? Which do you not agree with?

4 Discuss the questions with a partner. Use the sentences from exercise 1 to help you.

1 Which scenes in the story did you enjoy the most?
2 What bits of the story did you not like?
3 Who was your favourite character, and were there any characters who you did not like? Why?
4 What is your opinion of *The Prince and the Pauper*?

THE OXFORD BOOKWORMS LIBRARY

THE OXFORD BOOKWORMS LIBRARY is a best-selling series of graded readers which provides authentic and enjoyable reading in English. It includes a wide range of original and adapted texts: classic and modern fiction, non-fiction, and plays. There are more than 250 Bookworms to choose from, in seven carefully graded language stages that go from beginner to advanced level.

Each Bookworm is illustrated, and offers extensive support, including:

▸ a glossary of above-level words
▸ activities to develop language and communication skills
▸ notes about the author and story
▸ online tests

Each Bookworm pack contains a reader and audio.

6	**STAGE 6**	▸ 2500 HEADWORDS	▸ CEFR C1
5	**STAGE 5**	▸ 1800 HEADWORDS	▸ CEFR B2
4	**STAGE 4**	▸ 1400 HEADWORDS	▸ CEFR B1–B2
3	**STAGE 3**	▸ 1000 HEADWORDS	▸ CEFR B1
2	**STAGE 2**	▸ 700 HEADWORDS	▸ CEFR A2–B1
1	**STAGE 1**	▸ 400 HEADWORDS	▸ CEFR A1–A2
S	**STARTER**	▸ 250 HEADWORDS	▸ CEFR A1

Find a full list of *Bookworms* and resources at
www.oup.com/elt/gradedreaders

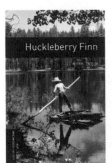

If you liked this Stage 2 Bookworm, why not try...

Huckleberry Finn
MARK TWAIN

Who wants to live in a clean house, wear clean clothes, be good, and go to school every day? Not young Huckleberry Finn, that is for sure.